GRADES 3–4

ARRANGED BY RACHEL JENNINGS

VIOLIN PART

DANNY BOY 3
YMCA 4
RUDOLPH THE RED-NOSED REINDEER 6
IT'S ONLY A PAPER MOON 7
KING OF THE ROAD 8
THE SLEEPING BEAUTY WALTZ 10
ON THE STREET WHERE YOU LIVE 12
SUMMER HOLIDAY 13
EYE OF THE TIGER 14
YOU'D BE SO NICE TO COME HOME TO 16

First published in 2010 by Faber Music Ltd
Bloomsbury House 74–77 Great Russell Street London WC1B 3DA
Music processed by Jackie Leigh
Cover design by Kenosha Design
Printed in England by Caligraving Ltd

ISBN10: 0-571-53426-0
EAN13: 978-0-571-53426-5

FOREWORD

Playing familiar pieces is always a pleasure, whether you've finally made it through *Twinkle Twinkle* or you're breaking hearts with *Schindler's List*, and there's little doubt that audiences feel the same. However, finding graded rock, pop and jazz arrangements which are rhythmically manageable yet melodically satisfying can be difficult, and this is particularly evident at intermediate level. *Red Hot Violin* was designed to address this issue, and offers today's violinists a vibrant collection of performance pieces which will appeal to players and audience alike.

Just as stylistic awareness and integrity is important in the interpretation of classical styles, it is equally so when preparing the popular pieces featured here. The overall feel or 'groove' of each arrangement is pivotal, and is provided by a strong and collaborative piano part which requires the familiarity of both players. Sufficient rehearsal time with your pianist is therefore essential prior to performance.

As musicians we pay a lot of attention to the art of performing, however the best understanding of any kind of music is gained by listening, and with internet access to Spotify and YouTube this is very easy to do. The recommended recordings listed with each piece suggest interpretations by well-respected artists, whereas the 'style guide' tracks illustrate the style of each arrangement itself, e.g. big band.

Above all, the purpose of the *Red Hot Violin* collection is to entertain, using a creative approach to showcase the traditional violin/piano partnership in a striking and contemporary way.

Rachel Jennings

KEY

These symbols alongside noteheads indicate slides, which are often used in jazz and fiddle music. This is an upward slide: begin the note roughly a semitone flat and rapidly slide your finger up to the printed pitch.

This is a downward slide. Begin to play the printed note before sliding your finger roughly a semitone flat.

This is a bend. Begin to play the printed pitch, then slide your finger flat and back up again to create a 'train whistle' effect.

(knock bow) Maintaining a regular bowhold, tilt the stick and either tap the wood against the C-bout or reach forwards to tap against the shoulder. Keep the stick close to the violin, and be gentle but firm enough for the sound to resonate. Be ready to return to arco.

DANNY BOY

LONDONDERRY AIR

This Irish air is one of the most-requested violin pieces; it will see you through weddings, funerals and Christmas with the aunties and uncles. *Danny Boy* comes in many shapes and sizes: traditional Celtic renditions, gorgeous brass band arrangements, even Elvis Presley has contributed. However, be aware that it's one of those pieces that *must* be played well, so really get it under your belt before you perform it. Keep your bows long and legato, and really sing out in the high bit – there won't be a dry eye in the house!

SUGGESTED RECORDING: Grimethorpe Colliery Band
STYLE GUIDE: *Last Night When We Were Young* by Marian McPartland

TRADITIONAL

YMCA

Recorded by the Village People in 1978, *YMCA* – and the dance which accompanies it – now have an absolute cult following. This arrangement begins misleadingly with a painfully slow stock fiddle intro, so ham it up and act like you're a total beginner – either very bad, or very bored – perhaps with a drooping violin to match? The main verse then kicks off very suddenly, so be ready, and really go for it! Swish your final upbow into the air like a pro – believe me, it'll look great.

SUGGESTED RECORDING: Village People
STYLE GUIDE: *Ernie (The Fastest Milkman In The West)* by Benny Hill

WORDS AND MUSIC BY HENRI BELOLO, JACQUES MORALI AND VICTOR WILLIS

2.
A little slower
a tempo
mf
2
f
(optional)
ff
f
ff
f
cresc.
ff

RUDOLPH THE RED-NOSED REINDEER

It had to be done; let's face it, Christmas wouldn't be the same without it, and if you whip out this jaunty, honorary carol – whether at the Christmas concert, the old folks' home or around the family tree – you can be sure you'll stay in Santa's good books for another year.

SUGGESTED RECORDING: Ella Fitzgerald
STYLE GUIDE: *Frosty the Snowman* by Perry Como

WORDS AND MUSIC BY
JOHNNY MARKS

IT'S ONLY A PAPER MOON

In this arrangement of a playful jazz standard, the violin and piano play fairly equal roles as they switch between melody and accompaniment. Try to be aware of which part you're playing. Use light, detached strokes, and play up the cheeky elements such as the 'train whistles' (bars 16 and 40), the pizzicato 'bass' at bar 24 and the piano's 'wrong notes' in bar 23. No vibrato for this one.

SUGGESTED RECORDING: Dizzy Gillespie and Stuff Smith
STYLE GUIDE: *Stormy Weather* by Oscar Peterson

WORDS BY E. Y. "YIP" HARBURG AND BILLY ROSE
MUSIC BY HAROLD ARLEN

KING OF THE ROAD

This piece is a roll-along country number from the 1960s which describes living hand-to-mouth in a very laidback, wry sort of way. The simple, casual swing style implies that this guy is actually a pretty cool customer, so try to put this across in your playing by making sure you don't rush; chances are you have more time than you think you do. Play out when it's your turn to pizz the bassline, and really smear those slides, particularly in the double-stops at bar 29. Keep vibrato to a minimum.

SUGGESTED RECORDING: Teddy Thompson and Rufus Wainwright
STYLE GUIDE: *Fever* by Elvis Presley

WORDS AND MUSIC BY
ROGER MILLER

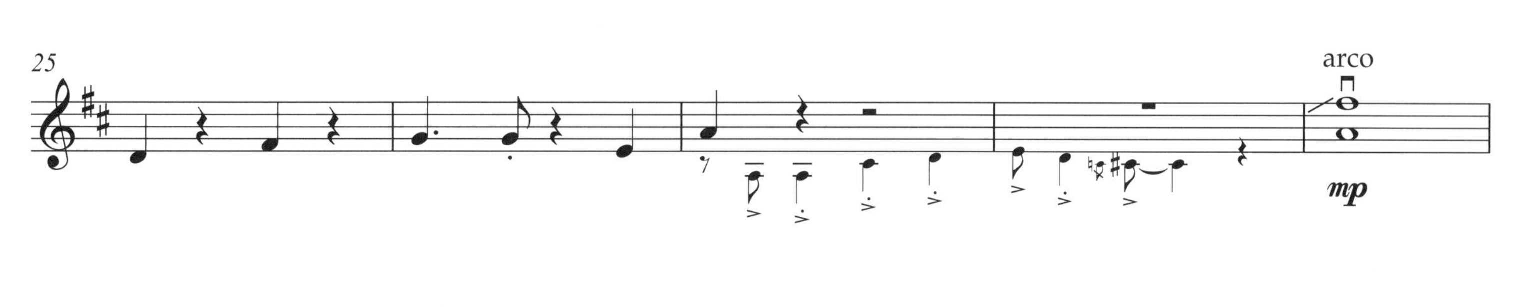
25
arco
mp

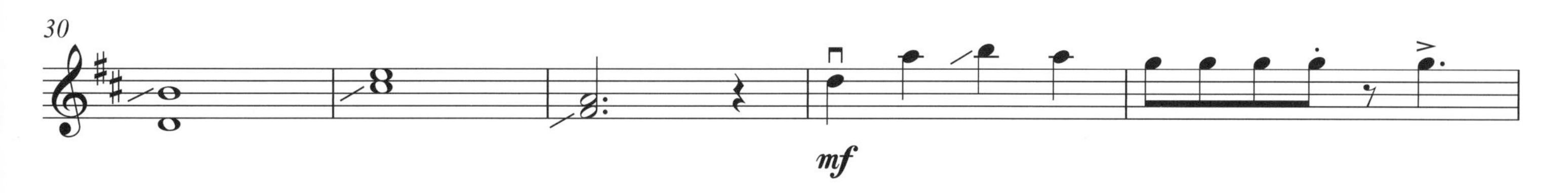
30
mf

35
(optional)
f

39

42
mp
f

45

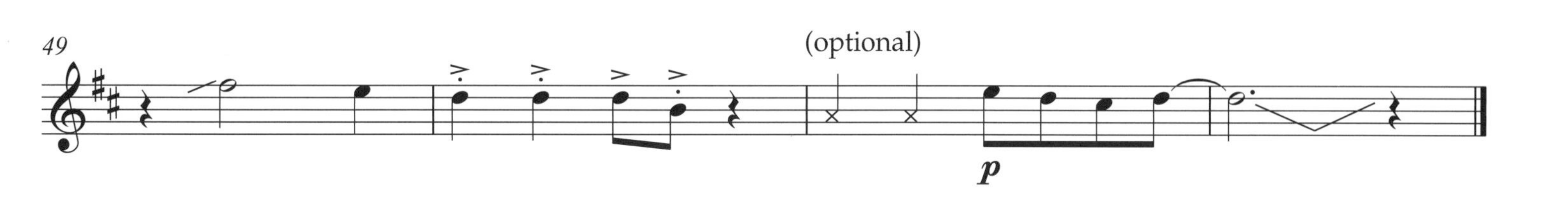
49
(optional)
p

THE SLEEPING BEAUTY WALTZ

Whether you've been to the ballet, seen the Disney animation (which adapted the melody for *Once Upon a Dream*) or even danced to it yourself, who can resist this famous and fabulously romantic waltz from Tchaikovsky's *Sleeping Beauty*? The trick with waltzes like this is to lean on (not necessarily accent) the downbeat, with a one-in-a-bar feel. Imagine yourself on a swing as you use lovely big legato bows for the main theme, and aim for a light, playful character at bar 45.

SUGGESTED RECORDING: Orchestra of the Royal Opera House, Covent Garden
STYLE GUIDE: Waltz from *Swan Lake* by Tchaikovsky

PYOTR ILYICH TCHAIKOVSKY

poco rit.
D.S. al Coda
CODA
allargando

ON THE STREET WHERE YOU LIVE

FROM 'MY FAIR LADY'

With its lovely, lyrical melody, this song from the classic 50s musical makes a great violin solo. Watch out for bars 20–21 where the harmony is unusual, and the key unfriendly: make sure you recover your position from the A♯ in order to place a good C♯, then the wide G♯. Bars 28–30 need to be really passionate, so take your time and milk it!

SUGGESTED RECORDING: 2001 London Cast (*My Fair Lady*)
STYLE GUIDE: *My Kind of Town* by Frank Sinatra

WORDS BY ALAN JAY LERNER
MUSIC BY FREDERICK LOEWE

Warmly ♩ = 88

mf *f* *mp* *f cantabile* *sub.* ***mp*** *f* *mf*

molto rall. *ff ad lib.*

a tempo III *restez* *mf* **rall.** *mp* *pp*

SUMMER HOLIDAY

This has been the UK's definitive (if somewhat idealistic) summer song since the 1960s, and this arrangement is quintessentially English to match – listen out for a few snippets along the way. Be cheerful and outgoing in your performance, and see if you can conjure up images of Wimbledon (in the rain); Pimm's on the lawn (in the rain); fish and chips on the beach (in the rain)... and where else to play it than the school summer concert (outside, of course, in the rain). It's a feel-good classic, and they'll love it.

SUGGESTED RECORDING: Cliff Richard and the Shadows
STYLE GUIDE: *Always Look on the Bright Side of Life* by Monty Python

WORDS AND MUSIC BY
BRUCE WELCH AND BRIAN BENNETT

EYE OF THE TIGER

Eye of the Tiger is right up there in the great canon of rock anthems; its distinctive opening chords and throbbing bassline are instantly recognisable. This arrangement may sound a little obscure at first as you chug away on your open D (you're the rhythm guitarist!), but once the piano comes in, trust me, your audience will cotton on. Really play the rock star when you perform this – confidence is everything. Check out singers like Robert Plant and Freddie Mercury for pointers.

SUGGESTED RECORDING: Survivor
STYLE GUIDE: *The Best* by Tina Turner

WORDS AND MUSIC BY
JAMES PETERIK AND FRANK SULLIVAN

26
30
ff
mf
mp
34
f
37
mp
40
f
44
47
(V)
fff
mf
mp
51
mf
mp
55
mf
ff

YOU'D BE SO NICE TO COME HOME TO

This 1940s song is simple but versatile, and has been recorded by many well-known artists in a variety of styles and tempi, from dreamy ballad to frenetic swing. The arrangement is easy-going and features a spare but independent piano part, which means that you will need to count accurately and trust that your pianist will be doing likewise... Try to create a clear contrast between the legato verse and the more animated solo, and steer clear of vibrato.

SUGGESTED RECORDING: Julie London
STYLE GUIDE: *I Love Paris* by Oscar Peterson

WORDS AND MUSIC BY
COLE PORTER